Naji Hakim
*1955

Gavotte

for Bassoon and Piano
für Fagott und Klavier
pour basson et piano

FAG 38
ISMN 979-0-001-20791-1

SCHOTT

Preface

The rondo form, the characteristic rhythm, the incipit of the melodic contour and the graceful mood of this gavotte are inspired by the 3rd Partita for solo violin in E major (BWV 1006) by Johann Sebastian Bach. The harmonic tonal style is expanded by chords with added notes and modulations to distant keys.

Vorwort

Die Rondoform, der charakteristische Rhythmus, der Beginn der melodischen Kontur und der graziöse Charakter dieser Gavotte sind von der dritten Partita für Solo-Violine in E-Dur (BWV 1006) von Johann Sebastian Bach inspiriert. Der harmonisch-tonale Stil wird ausgedehnt durch Anreicherung von Akkorden durch zusätzliche Töne und Modulationen in entfernte Tonarten.

Préface

La forme en rondeau, le rythme caractéristique, l'incipit du contour mélodique et le caractère gracieux de cette gavotte s'inspirent de la 3e Partita pour violon seul en mi majeur (BWV 1006) de Jean-Sébastien Bach. Le style harmonique tonal est élargi par des accords aux notes ajoutées et par des modulations à des tons éloignés.

Naji Hakim

To Delphine Constantin and Roman Reznik, with deep gratitude

Gavotte

Naji Hakim
*1955

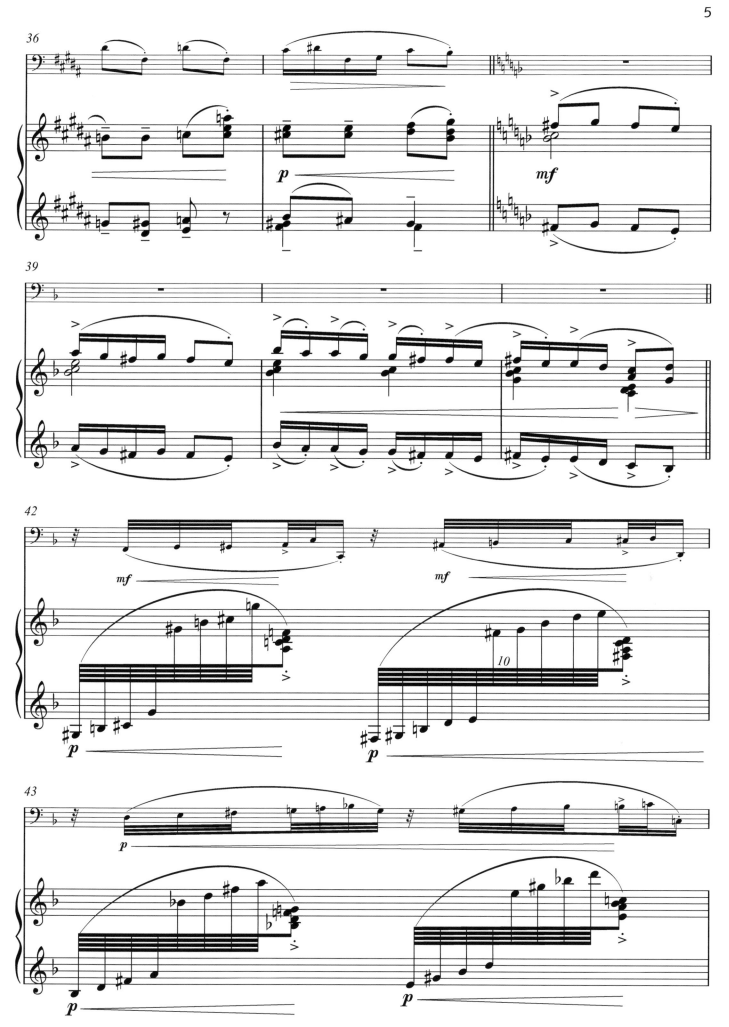

© 2019 Schott Music GmbH & Co. KG, Mainz · Printed in Germany

Bassoon

Gavotte

To Delphine Constantin and Roman Reznik, with deep gratitude

Naji Hakim
*1955

Tempo primo (♩ = 100)